NB DCPL0000549921   KT-132-236

Struck

Stage Makeup

by Cathy West

Ransom

StarStruck

Stage Makeup

by Cathy West

Illustrated by Martin Bolchover

Published by Ransom Publishing Ltd.
Radley House, 8 St. Cross Road, Winchester, Hants. SO23 9HX
www.ransom.co.uk

ISBN   978 184167 484 1
First published in 2011

Copyright © 2011 Ransom Publishing Ltd.

Illustrations copyright © 2011 Martin Bolchover

Photographic images copyright ©: cover – aldra; pages 4, 5 – Aleksandar Vrzalski; pages 6, 7 – Andrejs Zemdega, Greg Sargent, Alija, evirgen, Aftab Ali; pages 8, 9 – aldra, Christopher Snape; pages 10, 11 – Andrew Dorey, Antonis Papantoniou, Ercan Sucek, Jonathan Hill, Kevin Russ; pages 12, 13 – Charlie Brewer, Andrzej Burak, Emilia Kun, Pascal Genest; pages 14, 15 – Anja Peternelj, Derrick Tyson, Liza McCorkle, Jim DeLillo, Leo Kowal; pages 16, 17 – Nikada, vintagerobot, Hélène Vallée, Jill Chen; black satin, passim – Jon Helgason.

A CIP catalogue record of this book is available from the British Library.

The rights of Anita Loughrey and of Stephen Rickard to be identified as the authors and of Martin Bolchover to be identified as the illustrator of this Work have been asserted by them in accordance with sections 77 and 78 of the Copyright, Design and Patents Act 1988.

Stage Makeup

Contents

All About Stage Makeup

> " The best thing is to look natural, but it takes makeup to look natural. "
>
> Calvin Klein

Leabharlanna Poibli Chathair Bhaile Átha Cliath
Dublin City Public Libraries

What is stage makeup?

Q Why does an actor wear makeup on stage?

A So that they look more like the person they are playing. This could be:

- an older person

- a younger person

- or a person who looks different: a different hairstyle or hair colour.

Most plays also use stage lighting. This makes it even more important for actors to wear stage makeup.

Good lighting can make stage makeup look better.

Ancient Greek and Roman actors didn't use makeup. They wore masks instead.

Stage makeup is different from ordinary makeup.

Makeup for the theatre

In the theatre, the actor is on the stage. The audience is quite far away.

Actors wear makeup so that the audience can see their faces clearly.

Then the audience can see and understand the actor's facial expressions.

Theatre makeup looks good from far away. It looks very odd when you see it close-up.

Stage lighting is important, too. Lighting controls how the makeup looks in the play.

The lighting and the makeup must work together to get the best effect.

Makeup for film and television

Makeup for film and television is not like makeup for the theatre.

In a film the actor will be in different places – **indoors** and **outdoors**.

The film will have all kinds of shots – **close-ups, long shots.**

- The makeup must work for all kinds of shots.

- It must look **natural**.

- It must be **perfect**.

In the cinema, the audience might see a face in close-up. The face will be **huge**.

Bad makeup will show up easily!

Film and TV makeup is very important.

Every year there is an **Academy Award** for best film makeup.

Film and television pictures are getting better.

With HDTV, bad makeup is even easier to spot!

Many films now use computer graphics as well as actors.

Makeup artists need to work with computer graphics, too.

The black eye and blood is all makeup.

But it still has to look good in a close-up.

11

Trick

You can use makeup to change the shape of an actor's face.

 Make the cheekbones and nose brighter.

 Make the sides of the nose and the cheeks darker.

The person's face looks thinner.

Tip

Focus on makeup for eyes and eyebrows. Actors use their eyes to express feelings onstage.

12

Work with the lighting director to get the best effects. Good lighting helps good makeup.

Remember – nothing has any colour until light shines on it.

The colour of the light changes the colours you see.

Pink light makes makeup look warmer.

Red light ruins makeup.

Orange light makes flesh colours stronger.

Trick

Makeup on lips is important too.

The rule is: larger lips need a deeper lipstick colour.

13

Special effects makeup

People use makeup to create monsters and other fantasy creatures.

This is called special effects makeup.

Sometimes makeup artists use rubber or foam as part of the makeup. This is called prosthetic makeup.

You can use special effects makeup ...

To make people look much older.

To create monsters.

Or fantasy beasts.

Or witches. (Her nose is made of rubber or foam.)

A career as a makeup artist

Skills you need

A good stage makeup artist needs:

 to know about stage makeup

 to get on well with people

 to work well under pressure.

Where do I start?

You can study stage makeup at college. It's a good place to start.

But make sure they teach stage makeup. Some schools only teach makeup for the fashion industry.

Get experience

Work experience is the best training you can get.

Contact the **theatres** and **theatre groups** where you live. Find out if you can work there in your spare time.

Work for free if you need to. It's all good training!

It's your business

Most makeup artists are **freelance**. They get hired for each job.

So you need to be good at selling your **skills**.

You need photos of work you've done: you can show these to people. This is your **portfolio**.

17

Chapter One

Fed up

Rose and Jordan were both makeup artists. They worked for famous stars on TV and in the theatre.

Rose and Jordan were both very good at their jobs. But they could not agree who was the best.

'I'm the best makeup artist ever!' Rose said.

'No you're not! I'm the best!' said Jordan.

They argued all the time. All the actors were fed up with it. They complained to Milly, the director.

Milly talked to Rose and Jordan.

'We are all tired of you two arguing,' she said. 'It must stop.'

'There is only one way to settle this,' Rose said.

'How?' Jordan asked.

'We will have a competition.'

Milly was the director. She talked to her makeup artists.

Chapter Two

The competition

'What sort of competition?' Jordan asked.

'I know,' said Milly. 'There is a fancy dress party tonight. There will be a prize for the best fancy dress. You can both do the makeup for everybody at the party.'

'So – we get to do everyone's makeup?'

'Yes. The best makeup artist will be the person who does the makeup for the winner of the fancy dress competition.'

'OK,' said Rose. 'I'm sure I will win.'

Milly had an idea.

There is a fancy dress party tonight. You can do all the makeup for it.

The person who does the makeup for the winner of the fancy dress competition is the best makeup artist.

For the rest of the day Rose and Jordan did the makeup for the fancy dress party.

They did the makeup for zombies. They did the makeup for princesses. They did the makeup for vampires.

Everybody loved their makeup. They were all very happy.

'I wonder who will win,' Jordan said.

'Me, of course,' said Rose with a grin.

Chapter Three

The fancy dress party

There were lots of famous people at the party. They all loved the makeup Rose and Jordan had done for them.

At last, it was time to announce the winner of the competition. Rose and Jordan were very excited.

Milly spoke into a microphone.

'The winner of the fancy dress competition is …'

She paused and looked around at everybody.

'… the alien,' she said.

Everybody clapped and cheered.

It was a great party. At last it was time to announce the winner.

The winner of the fancy dress competition is ... **the alien!**

'Did you do the alien makeup?' Jordan asked Rose.

'No,' said Rose. 'Did you?'

'No,' Jordan said.

'Then who did?'

Jordan shrugged his shoulders. 'I don't know,' he said.

They were both very worried. Could there be a better makeup artist than them?

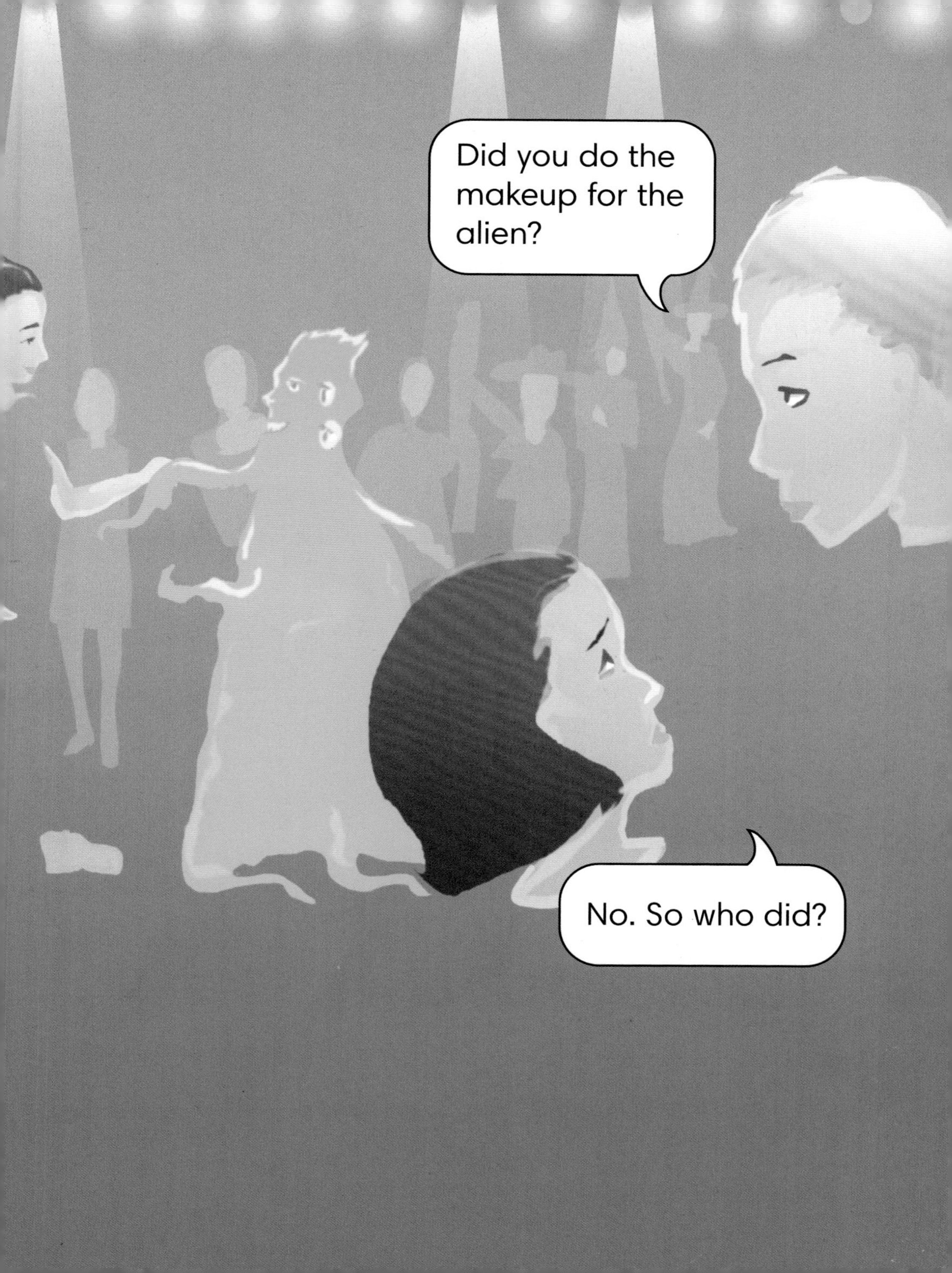
Did you do the makeup for the alien?
No. So who did?

Chapter Four

The mystery alien

Milly gave the prize for the fancy dress competition to the alien.

Rose and Jordan wanted to speak to the alien. They wanted to find out who had done his makeup.

They pushed their way through the crowd. But by the time they reached Milly, the alien had gone.

'So which one of you did the makeup for the alien?' Milly asked Rose and Jordan.

Rose and Jordan looked at each other.

'Neither of us did,' said Rose.

After the party, Rose, Jordan and Milly were walking home.

'Did you find out who did the makeup for the alien?' Milly asked.

'No,' Jordan said.

'Now we will never know who the best makeup artist is,' said Rose.

High in the sky, an alien spacecraft zoomed back to its own planet. An alien looked out of the window of the spacecraft.

'That was a great party,' thought the alien.

'But they do give prizes for strange things.'

34

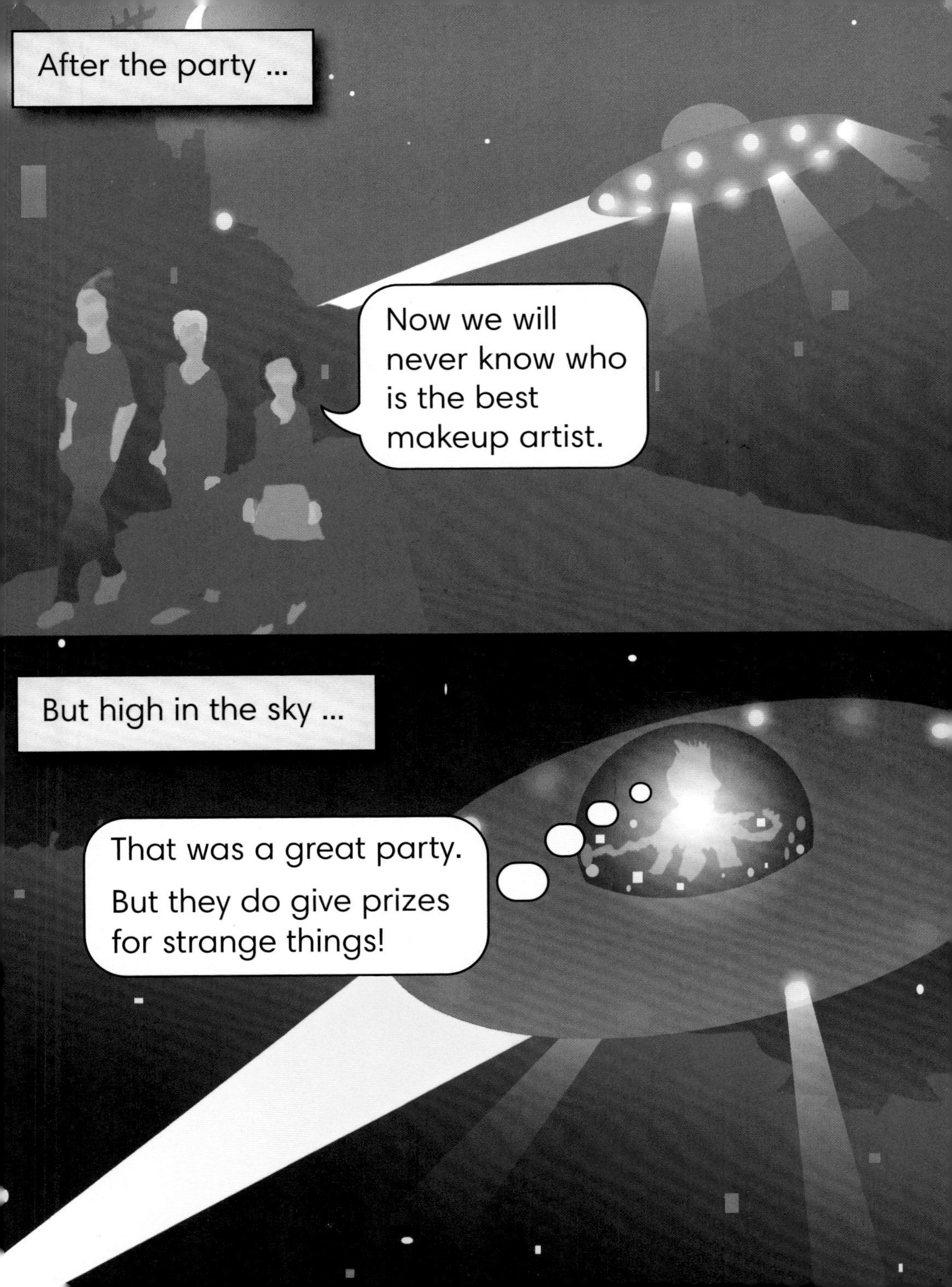

Academy Award

close-up shot

computer graphics

facial expressions

film and television
    makeup

freelance

hand-eye
    co-ordination

HDTV

lighting director

long shot

makeup artist

natural

portfolio

pressure

prosthetic makeup

special effects makeup

stage lighting

theatre makeup

work experience